SPEAK UP!

To the kids at school, Mia is the autistic girl who can't speak up.

To her mom, she's the fragile daughter who needs help fitting in.

But to thousands of fans watching her gain popularity online, Mia is a talented singer known only by her secret identity, Elle-Q, and she has a lot to say.

SPEAK UP!

REBECCA BURGESS

SCHOLASTIC INC.

ISBN 978-1-339-00644-4

12 11 10 9 8 7 6 5 4 3 2   23 24 25 26 27 28

Printed in the U.S.A.   40

First Scholastic printing, January 2023

The artist used Photoshop to create the illustrations for this book.

FOR AMANDA, LAURA, KATE, AND MOTH—
AS WE'VE GROWN UP TOGETHER, I'VE SEEN
YOU ALL FIND YOUR VOICES TOO!

CHAPTER ONE

2

11

12

I WONDER WHAT SHE LOOKS LIKE IN REAL LIFE?

ME TOO! AND THERE'S NO INFORMATION ABOUT HER ONLINE.

I'M SURE SHE ISN'T FROM AROUND HERE THOUGH. IF SHE WENT TO THIS SCHOOL, I KNOW WE WOULD BE FRIENDS.

ElleFan04

This is amazing! Elle-Q, when are you gonna do a live show?? I want to see you perform live sooo bad. Luv ya Elle-Q!

250 ❤   40 Replies

WizardSheepie

Loving Elle-Q right now

26

CHAPTER TWO

COLD CALM

I BET CHARLIE'S BEEN WAITING FOR ME GET ONLINE.

24 messages

HAHA! YUP!

Charlie

Mia OMG

Our new song is GOING VIRAL

Mia I can't believe it, our new song.

we're awesome.

MIA wHeRe Are yOu??

mmmmiiiiaaaaa

You gotta look at the Elle-Q page it's amazingg

omg mia it's been like AN HOUR

okayyy maybe more like 10 mins

HOW CAN I BE THE ONE DOING THE SINGING FOR ELLE-Q? YOU'RE THE ONE WHO DOES ALL THE TALKING.

Sorry, Mom was late picking me up. Let's talk on video chat?

Tap Tap
Tap Tap

MIA! I! AM! A MUSICAL GENIUS!

UUUH... HELLO TO YOU TOO.

MIA, HAVE YOU CHECKED OUT THE COMMENTS FOR "WARRIOR"? THE RESPONSE IS AMAAAZING!

YEAH, EVEN MY CLASSMATES WERE TALKING ABOUT IT TODAY. IT WAS SO WEIRD.

OF COURSE! THEY WERE THE INSPIRATION FOR THAT SONG, RIGHT?

LIKE I SAID. I'M A MUSICAL GENIUS.

CHARLIE...

...AND YOU KNOW, YOU TOO. WE MAKE A GREAT TEAM.

...HAVE YOU SEEN THIS ONE COMMENT BY ELLEFANO4?

YEAH, BUT...ASKING FOR A LIVE SHOW...

I KNOW! WE HAVE FANS NOW!

WOULDN'T THAT BE AWESOME? YOU SAW THAT TALENT SHOW POSTER ON OUR WAY TO SCHOOL, RIGHT?

BUT AT SCHOOL, WHEN THERE'S A LOT GOING ON...

...AND NEW ROUTINES, AND LOTS OF PEOPLE TO TALK TO—IT'S JUST TOO MUCH.

YOU'VE SEEN WHAT CONCERTS ARE LIKE. NO ONE WOULD WANT TO SEE ELLE-Q PERFORM IN A TALENT SHOW MADE TO BE COMFORTABLE FOR ME.

YAAAWWN

I'D JUST LOOK LIKE SOME KIND OF FREAK, ESPECIALLY COMPARED TO EVERYONE ELSE PERFORMING THERE...

AND I BET MY MOM WOULD GET ALL WEIRD ABOUT IT...

I REMEMBER A COUPLE OF YEARS AGO...

MY MOM TOOK ME TO A CONCERT TO SEE THE WEEKDYS.

STADIUM THIS WAY

BLEH, IT'S TOO HOT.

IT'S NOT 12:30 YET,

WHY ARE WE EATING NOW?

BUT THEN ONE THING AFTER ANOTHER STARTED STRESSING ME OUT MORE AND MORE.

THEN, JUST AS THE CONCERT STARTED...

MIA, DON'T STIM HERE.

I DON'T WANT TO DO THIS. WE NEED TO GO.

I NEED TO GO RIGHT NOW!

MOM...I-I FEEL SICK. I-I—

CHAPTER THREE

ElleFan04

I love this song so much Elle-Q. I totally relate! I feel like I'm an impostor too sometimes, like it's hard to know who you should be, I ttly get it. This song makes me want to be myself, no matter how I'm feeling.

I LOVE THESE COMMENTS FROM ELLEFAN. THEY REALLY GET WHAT MY LYRICS ARE ABOUT.

MIA, IF SOMEONE IS WEARING HEADPHONES

IT'S NICE TO HAVE SOMEONE UNDERSTAND ME FOR ONCE.

Haha.

THAT GENERALLY MEANS THEY CAN'T HEAR WHAT YOU'RE SAYING.

BESIDES, WE'RE NOT EVEN DOING A LIVE PERFORMANCE.

I DUNNO...I JUST THOUGHT, SINCE OUR MUSIC IS DOING SO WELL...AND WITH THAT TALENT SHOW COMING UP...IT WOULD BE THIS GREAT OPPORTUNITY FOR US BOTH.

WOULDN'T IT BE COOL TO CONNECT WITH MORE PEOPLE LIKE ELLEFAN04?

I totally relate! I feel like I'm an impostor too sometimes, like it's hard to know who you should be I ttly get it. This song makes me want to be myself, no matter how I'm feeling

I KNOW IT MAKES YOU NERVOUS, BUT THERE'S A DEADLINE FOR ENTERING THE TALENT SHOW. CAN'T WE AT LEAST TALK ABOUT THE IDEA OF—

MIAAA! IT'S TIME TO GET GOING. I HAVE ERRANDS TO RUN!

SORRY, CHARLIE! GUESS YOU GOTTA GO NOW! LET'S GO DOWNSTAIRS!

Charlie

Mia?
Can you talk?

Charlie

It's been two days :(
I want to talk to you.
We can't keep
avoiding talking
about this Mia.

SLAM!

New Messege from Charlie

BZZ

Mia, I want to talk about the talent show. The deadline for entering is pretty soon.

Charlie

Even if we don't do this show, you can't avoid talking about this forever. Fans aren't going to stop asking. Elle-Q could be the start of something really big. My music could turn into something really big.

and I do want to perform.
...I guess I don't know exactly
what I want.
Everyone will hate me when they
see the real me up there onstage.

CHAPTER FOUR

THE NEXT DAY . . .

HI, MIA!

U-UH! H-HELLO.

UM, ME AND MY FRIENDS NEED AN EXTRA PERSON FOR OUR SCIENCE PROJECT. WE WERE WONDERING IF YOU WANT TO JOIN OUR GROUP?

. . .

OH-UM—I-LET ME THINK...

UM, WELL...THAT WOULD BE—

?

UH, I GUESS YOU CAN GET BACK TO ME ABOUT IT LATER.

I ASKED HER, BUT I DON'T THINK SHE WANTS TO. SHE DIDN'T EVEN LOOK AT ME, SO I GUESS SHE'S NOT INTERESTED.

I MISS CHARLIE. THEY UNDERSTAND ME SO MUCH BETTER THAN ANYONE ELSE.

WE WERE NEXT-DOOR NEIGHBORS WHEN WE WERE LITTLE.

ONLY CHARLIE COULD'VE EVER BEEN FRIENDLY ENOUGH TO WANT TO START PLAYING WITH A WEIRDO LIKE ME WHO COULDN'T TALK TO ANYONE.

WHEN MY MOM AND DAD SEPARATED AND WE HAD TO MOVE, I WAS SO HAPPY WE WERE ONLY MOVING A FEW STREETS DOWN.

I COULDN'T IMAGINE MY LIFE WITHOUT THEM. WE DO SO MUCH TOGETHER.

WE STILL WALK TO SCHOOL TOGETHER EVEN THOUGH WE GO TO DIFFERENT PLACES!

IT FEELS WEIRD TO IGNORE CHARLIE'S MESSAGES. BUT...I JUST DON'T KNOW HOW TO TALK ABOUT THE TALENT SHOW WITH THEM...

OHMYGOSH!!

AAAAHHH! YOU GUYS!

YOU GUYS!!

WHAT IS IT??

EEE!!

I WAS JUST READING THROUGH COMMENTS ON THE NEWEST ELLE-Q VIDEO AND SAW SOMETHING AMAZING.

BobbyBigEyes_02

Loving your music rn :)
So are we gonna get a tour
at any point in the future?

30 ❤   Reply

Elle-Q

Thanks! You won't
have to wait too long–
live performance
coming soon!!

2k ❤

Tap
Tap
Tap

Charlie, why is there a
comment from ME on our
video saying a live show is
coming soon???

What's going on? I never said we were doing a live show?? And now all our fans are getting excited and they'll be so disappointed and I don't even know what's happening here??

OKAY, CLASS, GET YOURSELF INTO TEAMS PLEASE!

WHAT I DON'T UNDERSTAND ABOUT GYM...

...IS WHY THE TEACHERS ALWAYS TALK ABOUT HOW TEAM SPORTS ARE SUPPOSED TO BUILD "TEAM SKILLS" AND "GET US COMFORTABLE WORKING WITH PEOPLE WE DON'T GET ALONG WITH."

DOWN WITH "PLAYING NICE" IN SPORTS!

BUT TO ME THEY JUST SEEM LIKE AN EXCUSE FOR KIDS TO HATE ON EACH OTHER.

MIA, YOU HAVEN'T FOUND A TEAM YET? JOIN THIS TEAM, PLEASE.

YOU CAN'T BE A GOOD TEAMMATE IF YOU DON'T GET MORE INVOLVED. AND YOU'RE STILL GETTING THE RULES WRONG, SO PLEASE TRY TO LISTEN.

I DO LISTEN.

I CAN'T HELP IT IF I GET THE RULES MIXED UP. AND EVEN IF I DO GET IT RIGHT, MY CLUMSINESS MESSES IT UP ANY WAY!!

THANKS, EVERYONE! YOU CAN GO GET CHANGED NOW AND HEAD TO LUNCH WHEN YOU'RE READY.

Charlie

It was me, I wrote that reply. We need to talk Mia.

WELL—

I—

I—

ARGH! IF WE WERE A TEAM, YOU WOULDN'T HAVE WRITTEN THAT COMMENT, CHARLIE!!

BEEP

BEEP

. . .

HMPF!

79

WH-WH-WHAT DID YOU DO WITH MY CLOTHES!

Y-YEAH, BUT—BUT!

WHAT ARE YOU TALKING ABOUT? WHY WOULD WE DO ANYTHING WITH YOUR CLOTHES?

N-NO. I SAW YOU... L-LOOKING AT ME—

YEAH, AND? I CAN LOOK IF I WANT. DOESN'T MEAN ANYTHING.

I DIDN'T TAKE YOUR CLOTHES, OKAY?

YOU PROBABLY FORGOT THEM.

WHERE ARE YOUR CLOTHES, ROBOT GIRL?

YEAH, WHERE ARE THEY?

WHY? ARE WE GOING TO BREAK YOU OR SOMETHING?

CAN YOU ST-STOP, TALKING S-SO QUICKLY...

Y-YES! NO! THAT'S NOT—

SHHHHHH

AAAAH!

YIKES, STOP BEING SO DRAMATIC.

why are you making

FEELING SICK...

BODY SHAKING...

HEART RUSHING...

CALM DOWN...CAN'T STIM TO CALM DOWN.
YOU SHOULDN'T STIM IN PUBLIC.

CAN'T CALM DOWN!
IT'S NOT GOING AWAY!

JUST LEAVE ME ALONE!!

I WANT TO GO HOME! GO AWAY!!

AHHHH!!

AHHHHHH!!

I FEEL SO EMBARRASSED.

I HAVEN'T HAD A MELTDOWN IN A LONG TIME.

I KNOW HOW WEIRD I MUST LOOK WHEN I'M WALKING AROUND IN CIRCLES.

BUT IN THE MOMENT, EVERYTHING IS SO OVERWHELMING. I END UP FEELING SICK AND MY BODY REACTS BEFORE I EVEN GET A CHANCE TO TRY TO STOP IT.

WOULDN'T ANYONE REACT THE SAME, IF IT SEEMED LIKE THEY WERE FACING THE SCARIEST THING IN THE WORLD WITH NOWHERE TO ESCAPE?

AND YET...I ALWAYS FEEL SO STUPID AFTER MY BODY HAS FINALLY CALMED DOWN.

IF YOU TRIED HARDER TO HIDE YOUR STIMS, OR THINK ABOUT YOUR TONE OF VOICE—

MIA...I KNOW YOU'VE BEEN GETTING STRESSED RECENTLY.

I D-DON'T WANT TO TRY ANY NEW TECHNIQUES.

IT DOESN'T MATTER IF YOU DON'T WANT TO. THEY'LL BE GOOD FOR YOU.

TH-THEY DON'T... THEY DON'T FEEL GOOD. PRETENDING I'M NORMAL DOESN'T FEEL GOOD.

BUT IF YOU DON'T TRY TO ACT NORMAL, THEN YOU'LL NEVER GET TO THE POINT OF FEELING NORMAL.

I KNOW WHAT'S BEST FOR YOU, MIA.

I DON'T UNDERSTAND WHY YOU RESIST IT SO MUCH.

WHEN THE DOCTOR DIAGNOSED YOU, HE BARELY GAVE ME ANY INFORMATION.

I HAD NO IDEA WHAT TO DO, I JUST KNEW THAT YOU WERE STRESSED OUT ALL THE TIME AT SCHOOL, AND I WANTED TO FIX IT.

YOUR DAD WAS GONE AFTER THE DIVORCE, AND I HAD TO DEAL WITH THIS NEW LABEL FOR YOU ALL BY MYSELF.

autism help

I LOOKED ONLINE FOR WAYS TO HELP YOU, AND MOST WEBSITES FOR PARENTS SAID THE SAME THING.

autism help 🔍

How to cure Autism

Tips on getting rid of autistic behavior in children

"YOUR CHILD WILL CONTINUE WITH THIS UNHELPFUL BEHAVIOR THAT GIVES THEM SEVERE STRESS, UNLESS YOU INTERVENE."

"YOUR CHILD DOESN'T HAVE THE CAPACITY TO CONNECT WITH OTHERS."

"YOUR CHILD IS LIVING IN THEIR OWN LITTLE WORLD AND WILL ALWAYS BE ISOLATED AND LONELY."

Can autism ever go away?

Intervention services for Autism

ALL THOSE BOOKS AND WEBSITES SAID THE ONLY WAY YOU'D FIND LIFE EASIER WAS IF I FOUND WAYS TO TONE DOWN YOUR AUTISM SO THAT YOU CAN CONNECT BETTER WITH THE REST OF THE WORLD.

I JUST WANT YOU TO BE HAPPY, MIA. BUT YOU JUST SIT IN YOUR ROOM ALL DAY WITH CHARLIE WRITING IN THAT NOTEBOOK AND LAPTOP...

ElleFan04

Elle-Q, whenever I'm feeling bad I always watch your videos. You're so brave and strong, your lyrics inspire me to be brave and strong too. I feel like such a loser sometimes. I wish I could be more e you.

NEW EMAIL

NEW EMAIL

Talent show update!

HUH. THAT'S WEIRD. I'VE BEEN TRYING TO IGNORE THE TALENT SHOW, HOW AM I GETTING EMAILS FROM THEM??

OPEN EMAIL

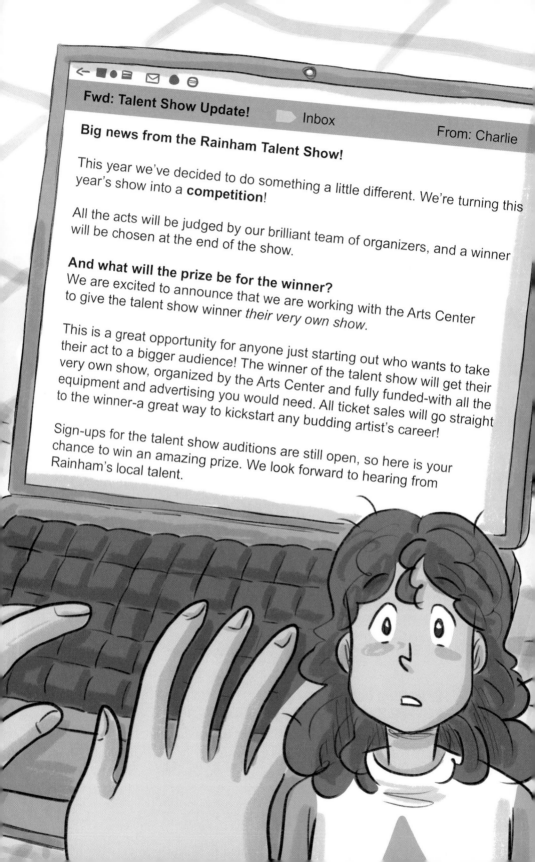

CHAPTER FIVE

HEY, MIA...

H-HEY...

. . .

U-UM...CHARLIE...

I'M...S-SORRY ABOUT EARLIER.

I WAS BEING SELFISH TO NOT LET YOU AT LEAST TALK THINGS THROUGH.

YOU WERE RIGHT... ABOUT WHAT YOU SAID...

I'VE BEEN SO WRAPPED UP IN MY OWN WORRIES, I DIDN'T THINK ABOUT WHAT YOU MIGHT WANT.

AND YOU HAVE A RIGHT TO SAY WHAT WE START DOING WITH OUR MUSIC.

UM, THAT'S WHY—

W-WHY—I WANTED TO L-LET YOU KNOW—

I-I—GOT THIS EMAIL—

THE TALENT SHOW IS GIVING PEOPLE A CHANCE TO HOST THEIR OWN SHOW.

?!

HOW DID YOU KNOW THAT?

HEH! I SAW THAT EMAIL A WHILE AGO, MIA...

...AND FINALLY DECIDED THAT YOU SHOULD SEE IT TOO.

SO I FORWARDED IT TO YOU! I'M SORRY I DIDN'T SAY ANYTHING WITH THE EMAIL. I THOUGHT YOU MIGHT IGNORE IT OTHERWISE.

From: Charlie

nt. We're turning this

UH! I WAS SO CAUGHT UP IN THE EMAIL I DIDN'T NOTICE WHO SENT IT!

WHEN THEY ANNOUNCED THAT PRIZE, SUDDENLY THIS WASN'T JUST SOMETHING WE COULD TRY OUT ANY YEAR. IT BECAME THIS BIG OPPORTUNITY THAT COULD BE AMAZING FOR US.

I KEPT TRYING TO BRING IT UP TO YOU—

BUT ANY TIME I MENTIONED PERFORMING AT THE TALENT SHOW, YOU CHANGED THE CONVERSATION OR TRIED TO AVOID ME!

I WAS JUST GETTING SO...FRUSTRATED. I WANTED TO TALK TO YOU ABOUT THIS.

SO THE OTHER DAY WHEN YOU STARTED IGNORING ME, IT'S LIKE I CAVED WHEN I WROTE THAT COMMENT.

I'M SORRY. I KNOW I SHOULDN'T HAVE WRITTEN THAT COMMENT. I KNOW IT WAS REALLY STRESSFUL FOR YOU—

IT'S OKAY, CHARLIE.

YOU'RE RIGHT. I'VE BEEN AVOIDING SOMETHING WE HAVE TO TALK ABOUT EVENTUALLY.

SHE DOESN'T THINK I CAN DO THINGS BY MYSELF.

Rainham Talent Show Form

DON'T WORRY, MY MOM WON'T FIND OUT.

IT'S FINE. I'LL JUST SIGN THE FORM AND SAY MY MOM SAID YES.

SHE DOESN'T CARE ABOUT ALL THE WRITING AND MUSIC I DO ANYWAY.

SHE ONLY EVER TALKS ABOUT HOW SHE WANTS ME TO BE LIKE EVERYONE ELSE.

Parent Permission Sign:

Chloe Tab|

Tap
Tap
Tap

WHOA, ARE YOU SURE ABOUT THAT?

...nham Tale
Show Form

By signing the below you hereby give permis... ...ur child, if under 18, to participate in ...uns and main performance of the Rainb... ...ent show. Please sign your name and s...

Name: Mia Tabolt Age: 12	Parent Permission Sign:
Are you performing by yourself or	Chloe Tabolt
If participating in a group, name of	

Email Sent!

HEY, MAYBE WE COULD DEBUT A NEW SONG AT THE TALENT SHOW. WHAT DO YOU THINK?

OH COOL! DO YOU KNOW WHAT SONG YOU WANNA DO?

OH, YOU'RE GOING NOW?

ISN'T IT A LITTLE TOO EARLY THOUGH?

I—UH—UH—I-I—UH—

I'M GOING TO A NEW WRITING CLUB, AND WE HAVE TO BE THERE BEFORE THE SCHOOL OPENS.

OH!

WELL, OF COURSE! THAT'S GREAT!

AAAHH! THIS IS WONDERFUL! GO YOU!

GO MAKE NEW FRIENDS, MIA. THIS WILL BE GREAT FOR YOU!

SLAM!

HAAAH.

LOOK AT YOU GETTING UP EARLY FOR ONCE!

....ARE YOU OKAY?

LYING TO MY MOM MAKES ME FEEL LIKE I'M HAVING A HEART ATTACK. I DON'T KNOW HOW PEOPLE CAN SAY IT'S EASY TO LIE—IT MAKES MY HEAD FEEL LIKE IT'S GONNA EXPLODE.

WELL, YOU'RE GONNA HAVE TO GET USED TO IT IF WE'RE GOING TO PERFORM IN A TALENT SHOW BEHIND HER BACK.

WE CAN PRACTICE FOR THE TALENT SHOW AUDITION AT MY HOUSE. THAT WAY YOU WON'T HAVE TO WORRY ABOUT YOUR MOM ASKING TOO MANY QUESTIONS.

RAINHAM TALENT SHOW! SIGN UP NOW!

RAINHAM TALENT SHOW! SIGN UP NOW!

YEAH...FIRST I NEED TO FOCUS ON GETTING THAT NOTEBOOK BACK...

WOULD IT REALLY BE THAT BAD IF SOMEONE SEES YOUR NOTEBOOK?

I DON'T HAVE FRIENDS LIKE YOU DO, CHARLIE. KIDS WILL USE THE NOTEBOOK AS AN EXCUSE TO MAKE FUN OF ME.

Y-YES.

BECAUSE— BECAUSE—BECAUSE—

BECAUSE! I'M THE TOP RUNNER ON MY SCHOOL'S TRACK TEAM.

OH! I WONDER WHY I DON'T REMEMBER YOU AT OUR LAST LOCAL COMPETITIVE—

DON'T REMEMBER ME?!

YOU MUST'VE NOT SEEN ME.

BELIEVE ME. YOU'D REMEMBER IF YOU SAW ME OUT THERE.

ANYWAY. MIA WAS SHOWING ME AROUND, SINCE I WAS THINKING OF DITCHING MY TRACK TEAM TO JOIN YOURS.

SINCE YOU HAVE BETTER RUNNING... EQUIPMENT.

OH REALLY?

WHA-?

WELL, PLEASE COME TO MY OFFICE. I CAN SHOW YOU WHAT WE HAVE TO OFFER.

COME ON, CHARLIE! I'LL SHOW YOU THE LOCKER ROOMS OKAY?!

FEEL FREE TO TALK TO ME IF YOU HAVE ANY QUESTIONS.

OKAY!! THANKS!

CHARLIE!! L-LAURA! LAURA, SH-SHE'S IN THE LOCKER AREA! IF SHE SEES ME OR MY NOTEBOOK, SHE'LL...SHE'LL!!

DON'T GO INTO LOST AND FOUND. DON'T GO INTO LOST AND FOUND. DON'T GO INTO LOST AND FOUND.

WHY IS SHE JUST STANDING THERE?

PHEW!

CHARLIE, THIS IS EXACTLY WHAT I DIDN'T WANT.

LAURA'S GOING TO PICK ON ME SO MUCH!

I'D BETTER GET GOING, OTHERWISE I WON'T GET TO SCHOOL ON TIME.

I'M SORRY, MIA...

THIS IS TORTURE.

ABSOLUTE TORTURE.

I'VE BEEN READING THROUGH IT...

...AND HONESTLY? I THINK...THIS MIGHT BE ELLE-Q'S NOTEBOOK.

WHAT?

WHAT?

WHAT?!

NO. WAY.

LET ME SEE!!

OKAY, BUT, JUST READ SOME OF THE STUFF WRITTEN IN THERE. LIKE IT'S ALL THE BEGINNINGS OF ALL HER SONGS. IT HAS TO BE HER, RIGHT? RIGHT??

...I THINK YOU'RE RIGHT.

OH MY GOSH.

THIS IS THE BIGGEST NEWS EVER!!

IF THIS REALLY IS ELLE-Q'S NOTEBOOK...

...THEN THAT MEANS SHE GOES TO THIS SCHOOL...

...AND I HAVE ALL THE CLUES I NEED RIGHT HERE...

...TO FIND ELLE-Q'S SECRET IDENTITY.

CHAPTER SIX

NOW THAT SHE KNOWS IT'S ELLE-Q'S NOTEBOOK, I CAN'T STOP WORRYING ABOUT HER DISCOVERING WHO I AM...

IMAGINE IF SHE FOUND OUT AND TOLD EVERYONE.

IT WOULD BE ANOTHER REASON TO PICK ON ME. I'M SURE MY WHOLE GRADE WOULD STOP WATCHING OUR VIDEOS...

WELL, YOU JUST GOTTA FIND A WAY TO GET THAT NOTEBOOK BACK, RIGHT?

OKAY, WE'RE ALL SET UP! LET'S DO THIS.

I NEED TO GET TO SCHOOL IN LIKE TEN MINUTES.

Y-YUP.

HEY, EVERYONE! I'VE GOT A BIG ANNOUNCEMENT. WE'RE ENTERING THE RAINHAM TALENT SHOW!

THE SHOW IS JUST A MONTH AWAY. YOU MIGHT GET A CHANCE TO SEE US PERFORM LIVE! BUT, WE HAVE TO AUDITION FIRST.

LAURA?!

WHOOOA. HOW DID SHE FIND OUR SECRET FILMING SPOT??

WELL, I GUESS NOW SHE KNOWS YOU LIVE LOCALLY...

I THINK I WROTE THE ALLEY DOWN IN THE NOTEBOOK ONCE, BUT ONLY THE ALLEY NAME!

WOW. SHE'S WAY SMARTER THAN YOU MAKE HER OUT TO BE.

Notification
New video from Elle-Q

UM, YOU GUYS. I KNOW MIA'S REALLY WEIRD...

BUT, MAYBE WE SHOULD LAY OFF HER A LITTLE.

OH, COME ON. SHE'S AUTISTIC—SHE DOESN'T CARE ABOUT STUFF LIKE THAT. SHE PROBABLY DOESN'T EVEN KNOW WE'RE GOOFING ON HER. YOU KNOW I'M ONLY JOKING AROUND.

I DON'T KNOW, JESS. YOU SAW HOW SHE REACTED IN GYM CLASS LAST WEEK...

YOU'RE TAKING THIS WAY TOO SERIOUSLY, LAURA!

W-WHAT?!

FRIENDS DON'T MAKE A BIG DEAL OUT OF A STUPID JOKE AND GET ANGRY.

U-UM, Y-YEAH. ACTUALLY...

NO. WAY.

YOU HAVE TO TELL ME!

...I-I HAVE AN IDEA OF WH-WHO IN OUR SCHOOL ELLE-Q MIGHT BE.

PLEASE TELL ME WHAT YOU KNOW.

IF YOU TELL ME EVERYTHING, MAYBE WE CAN FIND OUT WHO SHE IS TOGETHER.

THIS IS TOO WEIRD. WHY IS SHE SUDDENLY TREATING ME LIKE AN ACTUAL HUMAN BEING?

OHMYGOSH, OKAY! YOU GOTTA TELL ME ALL YOUR THEORIES! MEET ME IN THE LIBRARY AFTER SCHOOL, OKAY?

BUT IF IT'LL HELP THROW HER OFF TRACK AND AWAY FROM ME...

U-UM...OKAY.

...O-OOKAAAY?

W-WHOA...Y-YOU'VE REALLY BEEN WORKING HARD AT THIS.

I'M NOT STALKING HER OR ANYTHING. I'M NOT A LOSER, OKAY?

N-NO! I-I-I DIDN'T! I—UH—I... JUST NEVER MET ANYONE WHO LIKES ELLE-Q THIS MUCH.

W-WELL, OF COURSE I DO! ELLE-Q IS INSPIRATIONAL. I WOULDN'T EXPECT SOMEONE LIKE YOU TO UNDERSTAND—

AH. I-I MEAN...

U-UM. WHAT DO YOU FIND SO INSPIRING ABOUT ELLE-Q?

HER LYRICS ARE SO POWERFUL! THEY MAKE ME FEEL LIKE I CAN DO ANYTHING!

BUT THEY'RE, LIKE, EMOTIONAL TOO, FULL OF ALL THESE FEELINGS. SO I FEEL LIKE I CAN REALLY RELATE TO HER, EVEN IF SHE IS LIKE THIS SUPERHERO OR WHATEVER.

I HAVE TO GO. THAT WAS ACTUALLY, LIKE...FUN!

Y-YEAH...

I HAD NO IDEA YOU COULD ACTUALLY TALK, Y'KNOW, MORE THAN, LIKE, A FEW SENTENCES.

OH, WELL...WHEN IT'S SOMETHING I REALLY LOVE, I FIND IT EASIER TO TALK. AND WHEN IT'S NICE AND QUIET.

OH, RIGHT...

OOOH! DO YOU WANT ME TO GO THROUGH SOME SOCIALIZING TECHNIQUES WITH YOU? YOU KNOW, TOPICS TO BRING UP? KNOWING WHEN TO LET SOMEONE ELSE TALK?

NO, MOM, I'M FINE. WE HAVE LOTS TO TALK ABOUT.

THE RESPONSE TO OUR VIDEO HAS BEEN AMAZING. I'VE GOT A GOOD FEELING ABOUT THE AUDITION, MIA!

OH, THAT'S GREAT! I'M KINDA NERVOUS ABOUT THE AUDITION, BUT IT'LL BE GOOD PRACTICE I GUESS.

NERVOUS? WE'RE GONNA BE AMAZING!

DID YOU START WORKING ON LYRICS FOR THE DEBUT YET?

Hey Laura!
I'll be at your
house in 10 min

AHAHAHA!

CAN YOU BELIEVE OUR ENGLISH TEACHER THOUGHT ANYONE WOULD ACTUALLY SIGN UP TO DO POETRY READINGS IN THE AFTER SCHOOL DRAMA CLUB? NO WAY AM I GOING TO THAT NEXT WEEK.

ENGLISH IS ENOUGH OF A CHORE WITHOUT HAVING TO DO IT AFTER SCHOOL IN FRONT OF LOADS OF PEOPLE. I DON'T EVEN CARE IF I GET EXTRA CREDIT.

I MEAN, PLEASE!

I HAVE ENOUGH DRAMA IN MY LIFE WITH JESS. I DON'T NEED TO TAKE PART IN A SCHOOL CLUB FOCUSED ON IT!

HAHA!

I DON'T GET WHY YOU HANG OUT WITH JESS IF SHE'S REALLY THAT BAD.

OR WHY YOU IGNORE ME WHEN YOU'RE AROUND HER. WE GET ALONG PRETTY WELL... BUT AT SCHOOL IT'S AS IF WE'VE NEVER HUNG OUT LIKE THIS.

Sometimes I can't speak, The words are jumbled in my head

Sometim... world is... overcu...

WHAT ARE YOU WORKING ON?

N-NOTHING!

OH...

SO, LIKE, I HAD THIS IDEA FOR OUR ELLE-Q INVESTIGATION.

YOU KNOW THOSE POETRY READINGS WE WERE INVITED TO TOMORROW FOR THE DRAMA CLUB?

O-OH YEAH...

AND I'VE LISTENED TO ELLE-Q'S VOICE SO MUCH, I CAN RECOGNIZE IT FROM A MILE OFF. IT'S A GREAT IDEA, RIGHT? YOU'LL COME TOO, RIGHT?

I KNOW I SAID I DIDN'T WANT TO GO, BUT I WAS THINKING IT WOULD BE A GOOD CHANCE TO REALLY LISTEN TO EVERYONE'S VOICES. ESPECIALLY WHEN THEY'RE IN PERFORMANCE MODE. IT'LL NARROW DOWN OUR FINDINGS.

Y-YEAH!! SURE!! GREAT!!

NOT GREAT! NOT GREAT!!

SO, SHOULD WE MEET AT THE END OF DOVE STREET AFTER SCHOOL TOMORROW?

MIA?

...

MIA?

MIA??

MIA!!

WHA— OH. SORRY.

I SAID, DO YOU WANT TO MEET ON DOVE STREET TOMORROW AFTER SCHOOL?

THE TALENT SHOW AUDITIONS START AT 4:45, SO THAT'LL GIVE US PLENTY OF TIME TO—

UM, CHARLIE? I'M SUPPOSED TO BE DOING SOMETHING ELSE TOMORROW AFTER SCHOOL.

OH YEAH, THE AUDITION!

WHAT?

I COULD, BUT...I...

WELL, MY ENGLISH CLASS WAS INVITED TO THIS DRAMA CLUB THING. IT'S EXTRA CREDIT FOR MY GRADE. AND LAURA WANTS TO USE IT TO FIGURE OUT WHO ELLE-Q IS. AND IF I GO, I CAN STEER HER OFF TRACK. AND IF I DON'T GO THEN SHE MIGHT REALIZE THAT ELLE-Q IS ME—

CAN'T YOU GET OUT OF IT?

...WANT TO KEEP ON TOP OF THIS STUFF WITH LAURA. WHAT IF IT GETS OUT OF CONTROL? ...I MEAN, MAYBE YOU COULD DO THE AUDITION BY YOURSELF? PLAY YOUR GUITAR? THAT WOULD BE ENOUGH, RIGHT?

WHAT?! BUT—

I COULD REALLY USE YOUR HELP.

YEAH, I GUESS...

. . .

...SURE. DON'T WORRY, MIA, YOU CAN RELY ON ME.

HEE.

YES!

WE'RE IN! WHOOO!

...UH, I'M AUTISTIC. AND I TEND TO GET OVERLOADED BY BRIGHT LIGHTS AND TOO MUCH NOISE.

WHILE WE'RE HERE, DO YOU HAVE ANY QUESTIONS ABOUT THE SHOW?

SO...I-I WAS WONDERING IF I COULD HAVE THE LIGHTS TURNED DOWN WHEN I'M ONSTAGE TO FEEL MORE COMFORTABLE, AND BE ALLOWED TO WEAR HEADPHONES AND SOME COMFY CLOTHES, AND GO BAREFOOT TOO...?

OH—UH—

A-ACTUALLY...

...SOUNDS LIKE IT'S GOING TO BE A BORING SHOW...

YOU'RE BEING SO OVER-THE-TOP...

YIKES! GET OVER IT!!!

SURE, THAT'S TOTALLY FINE.

LET ME KNOW IF YOU THINK OF ANYTHING ELSE. MAYBE SOME EXTRA EQUIPMENT FOR YOUR LAPTOP, THERE?

O-OKAY!

WOW. SHE DIDN'T EVEN MAKE A BIG DEAL OUT OF ME TELLING HER I'M AUTISTIC.

WE'LL SEE YOU IN A COUPLE OF WEEKS.

WE DID IT, WE DID IT, WE DID IT!!

IT'S NOT TOO LATE YET. WANNA COME OVER TO MY HOUSE AND SHOOT AN ANNOUNCEMENT VIDEO?

WE DID IT!!

Our first live performance coming soon, details below!

Woot congratulations! Well done Elle-Q!

Yesss now some of us can FINALLY see ElleQ live aaahhhh

ON WITH THE SHOW I wish I lived close by so I could goooo

New Comment

ElleFan04

Congrats aaahhhhh! And just imagine if you win the competition? Then you'll get a WHOLE SHOW and we'll all get the chance to see you even more!!

200+ comments

CHAPTER SEVEN

TALENT SHOW!

Talent show in 2 weeks!

RAINHAM TALENT SHOW

Only three days to go!

Have you got your ticket yet?

Talent Show

Tomorrow!!

Talent show tomorrow, wish us luck!!!

I AM SO BORED. I THINK I NEED SOME NEW FRIENDS. WHEN IS EVERYBODY ELSE GOING TO GET HERE?

174

OH MY GOSH, LAURA. YOU HAVE TO LOOK AT THIS.

HAHAHA! LOOK, ROBOT GIRL'S A POET IN DISGUISE!

HAHA...YEAH...

AHAHAHA! I CAN'T BELIEVE YOU ACTUALLY TRIED TO WRITE SOMETHING. THE GIRL WHO NEVER TAL—

JESS! I—UH—

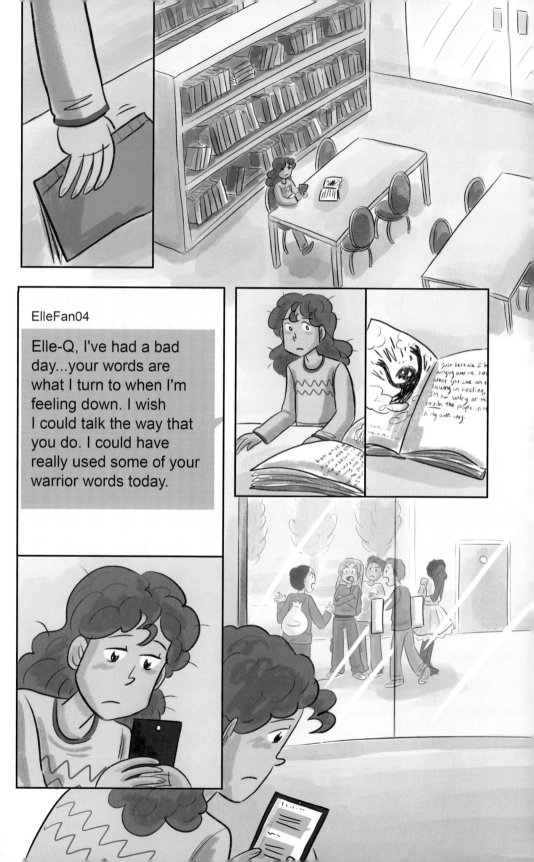

ElleFan04

Elle-Q, I've had a bad day...your words are what I turn to when I'm feeling down. I wish I could talk the way that you do. I could have really used some of your warrior words today.

181

CAN I...TAKE A LOOK?

CHAPTER EIGHT

BYE, MOM!

BYE, MIA!

I'VE GOT NOTHING TO BE NERVOUS ABOUT REALLY.

I MEAN, I STOOD UP TO JESS YESTERDAY, AND SHOWED LAURA MY NEW SONG.

IF I CAN DO THAT, I CAN SING IN FRONT OF PEOPLE ONSTAGE EASILY.

IF WE WIN, WE COULD GET TO DO OUR OWN SHOW AND EVERYTHING...

AND THE TALENT SHOW IS TAKING PLACE... TONIGHT?

MIA...I...WHAT?

A...A LIVE SHOW?

OH NO, I BROKE MOM!

PERFORMING? IN FRONT OF OTHER PEOPLE?

CHAPTER NINE

DON'T WORRY, I'M SURE MIA WILL BE HERE ANY MINUTE.

I'LL CALL HER AGAIN.

WHAT AN AMAZING ACT THAT WAS! OUR JUDGES ARE GOING TO HAVE A HARD TIME DECIDING WHO WILL WIN THEIR OWN SHOW.

JUDGES

WE HAVE MANY MORE ACTS TO GET THROUGH, SO LET'S MOVE ON TO OUR NEXT ONE!

COME OOON, MIAAA...

UUURGH.
I KNOW, CHARLIE.
I KNOW.

I CAN'T TALK TO
CHARLIE RIGHT NOW.
IF I TEXT THEM,
THEY'LL JUST TRY
TO CALL ME. I'LL
EMAIL INSTEAD.

ARGH! WRITING IS AS HARD AS TALKING IN THIS SITUATION.

New comment from ElleFan04

I'LL JUST TAKE A MINUTE TO READ THIS.

ELLEFAN ALWAYS MOTIVATES ME.

ElleFan04

Elle-Q, I can't wait to watch you in the talent show tonight. I had such a bad day today, I know you'll help make it better.
Read More

Juine20

Good luck with the talent show!
You'd better WIN!!
Youre the best!!

Elle-Q, I can't wait to watch you in the talent show tonight. I had such a bad day today, I know you'll help make it better.

AW, ELLEFAN.

I'M SORRY YOU HAD A BAD DAY. YOU'RE NOT THE ONLY ONE.

Can I make a confession? In real life, I sometimes pick on this girl at school. You always talk about being brave and strong. And I really try, but honestly, I never feel brave or strong in real life.

I have no confidence at all, and I always worry about what my friends think of me. That's why I pick on this girl. I feel so bad about myself, I end up making fun of her to make myself look and feel better.

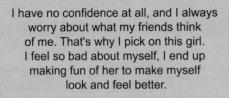

But the truth is, I'm jealous of her.

She's always just herself at school, no matter what others think of her.

She acts weird but doesn't seem to care.

Today, my friend shared something this girl had written with my other friends and they made fun of her.

I tried to stop her from doing it. Even yesterday I begged her to not do it. But when it happened, this girl thought it was all my fault.

She got really angry at me and accidentally pushed me.

We're waiting to go home early from school right now. I really don't blame her for thinking it was me. Even though we've been hanging out a lot...I haven't been a good friend to her. I'm such a coward. I let things get out of hand.

222

I wish I didn't care about what others think in the way she does, Elle-Q. I wish could be brave like her.

I really don't blame her for thinking it was me. Even though we've been hanging out a lot...I haven't been a good friend to her. I'm such a coward. I let things get out of hand. **I wish I didn't care about what others think in the way she does, Elle-Q. I wish I could be brave like her.**

I'm also sorry about blaming you for what Jess did.

I didn't realize you tried to stop her. I shouldn't have jumped to conclusions so quickly, not after how much we've hung out together.

Wait, I never told you that. How did you know??

HAHA!

Well, I read it in a comment you left me online. Just so you know, I don't hate you.

OH...MY...

Laura...I have something important to tell you.

OH.

HELLO?

OHMYGOSH, MIA!! YOU'RE ELLE-Q?!

229

...I CAN'T DO THIS TO HER.

OH MY GOODNESS.

I'LL GET YOU TWO TO YOUR SHOW ON TIME, I PROMISE.

UM, I'LL GO WAIT OUTSIDE FOR YOU TWO...

LAURA, I KNOW YOU ALREADY GOT A TICKET FOR THE TALENT SHOW...BUT DO YOU WANNA GET A SPECIAL BACKSTAGE VIEW?

REALLY?? OHMYGOSHHH!

MIA...I'M SORRY ABOUT EARLIER.

I-I WAS JUST... I WAS WRONG ABOUT YOU.

I'VE ALWAYS WORRIED ABOUT YOU.

YOU'RE SO DIFFERENT THAN ME...

I WAS NEVER SURE IF I WAS BEING THE BEST PARENT TO YOU.

I DON'T WANT YOU TO BE MISERABLE.

IT CAN BE STRESSFUL, HAVING TO TRY AND FIGURE OUT IF YOU'RE HAPPY ENOUGH WITHOUT BEING ABLE TO MEASURE IT AGAINST HOW OTHER KIDS ARE DOING.

SO I GUESS IT MEANS THAT I CAN BE A LITTLE...OVER-PROTECTIVE.

I'M SORRY TOO, MOM. FOR LYING TO YOU AND FIGHTING WITH YOU.

I KNOW THAT YOU WORRY ABOUT ME.

BUT I GUESS...I DON'T WANT TO BE PROTECTED.

JUST BECAUSE I'M DIFFERENT THAN YOU, AND DON'T HAVE MANY FRIENDS, AND FREAK OUT SOMETIMES...

...THAT DOESN'T MEAN I'M MISERABLE.

IT DOESN'T MEAN I HAVE TO ACT MORE LIKE EVERYONE ELSE.

I THINK...I LIKE BEING ME. I LIKE WHO I AM AND HOW I EXPRESS THAT IN MY OWN WAY.

UH, I THINK WE'D BETTER GET INSIDE SOON.

...WHAT DO YOU THINK?

I THINK YOU LOOK GREAT.

AND I'M GLAD YOU'RE HAPPY.

IF EXPRESSING YOURSELF IN WHATEVER WAY YOU WANT WILL HELP WITH THAT, I WILL ALWAYS SUPPORT YOU...EVEN IF IT MEANS YOU'LL HAVE TO DO SCARY THINGS SOMETIMES.

YOU ALL READY, MIA?

N-NOT REALLY, NO!

AW, HEY, I'LL BE THERE RIGHT BESIDE YOU. WE'RE IN THIS TOGETHER!

I'LL JUST...BE MYSELF.

ROOOOAAAAR

IT MEANS THE WORLD TO ME. I GUESS NONE OF US ARE...AS DIFFERENT AS I THOUGHT WE WERE.

REBECCA BURGESS is a comic artist and illustrator working in the UK, creating award-winning published and small press work. Along with drawing comics for their day job, Rebecca also loves drawing webcomics in their free time. Being autistic, they are particularly passionate about bringing more autistic characters into comics and stories! Outside of drawing comics and cuddling their cat, Rebecca also loves playing RPGs with friends, going on deep dives into history, and growing vegetables in their humble Bristol garden.